OFFICIAL

PAST
PAPERS
WITH ANSWERS

INTERMEDIATE 2

ENGLISH
2008-2012

✕SQA

BrightRED
PUBLISHING

© Scottish Qualifications Authority
All rights reserved. Copying prohibited. No part of this publication may be reproduced, stored in a retrieval system, or transmitted in any form or by any means, electronic, mechanical, photocopying, recording or otherwise.

First exam published in 2008.
Published by Bright Red Publishing Ltd, 6 Stafford Street, Edinburgh EH3 7AU
tel: 0131 220 5804 fax: 0131 220 6710 info@brightredpublishing.co.uk www.brightredpublishing.co.uk

ISBN 978-1-84948-270-7

A CIP Catalogue record for this book is available from the British Library.

Bright Red Publishing is grateful to the copyright holders, as credited on the final page of the Question Section, for permission to use their material. Every effort has been made to trace the copyright holders and to obtain their permission for the use of copyright material. Bright Red Publishing will be happy to receive information allowing us to rectify any error or omission in future editions.

2008

[BLANK PAGE]

X115/201

NATIONAL QUALIFICATIONS 2008	THURSDAY, 15 MAY 1.00 PM – 2.00 PM	ENGLISH INTERMEDIATE 2 Close Reading

Answer all questions.

30 marks are allocated to this paper.

Read the passage carefully and then answer **all** the questions, **using your own words as far as possible**.

The questions will ask you to show that:

> you understand the main ideas and important details in the passage—in other words, **what** the writer has said (**Understanding–U**);

> you can identify, using appropriate terms, the techniques the writer has used to get across these ideas—in other words, **how** he has said it (**Analysis–A**);

> you can, using appropriate evidence, comment on how effective the writer has been—in other words, **how well** he has said it (**Evaluation–E**).

A code letter (U, A, E) is used alongside each question to identify its purpose for you. The number of marks attached to each question will give some indication of the length of answer required.

Afar, far away

Matthew Parris describes the harsh conditions of life in North Africa, and suggests what may be in store for the region and the nomadic (wandering) people who live there.

At the beginning of this month I was in a hellish yet beautiful place. I was making a programme for Radio 4 about one of the world's most ancient trade routes. Every year, since (we suppose) at least the time of the Ancient Greeks, hundreds of thousands of camels are led, strung together in trains, from the highlands of Ethiopia into the Danakil
5 depression: a descent into the desert of nearly 10,000 feet, a journey of about 100 miles. Here, by the edge of a blue-black and bitter salt lake, great floes of rock salt encrusting the mud are prised up, hacked into slabs and loaded on to the camels.

Then the camels and their drivers make the climb through dry mountains back into the highlands, where the slabs are bound with tape and distributed across the Horn of
10 Africa. The camels drink only twice on their journey, walking often at night, and carrying with them straw to eat on the way back. Their drivers bring only dry bread, sugar and tea.

Travelling with the camel trains in mid-winter, when temperatures are bearable, I found the experience extraordinarily moving. But my thoughts went beyond the salt trade, and
15 were powerfully reinforced by the journey that followed it—to another desert, the Algerian Sahara.

These reflections were first prompted by a chance remark that could not have been more wrong. Our superb Ethiopian guide, Solomon Berhe, was sitting with me in a friendly but flyblown village of sticks, stones, cardboard and tin in Hamed Ela, 300ft below sea
20 level, in a hot wind, on a hot night. An infinity of stars blazed above. The mysterious lake was close, and when the wind changed you could smell the sulphur blowing from a range of bubbling vents of gas, salt and super-heated steam. On the horizon fumed the volcano, Hertale. With not a blade of grass in sight, and all around us a desert of black rocks, the Danakil is a kind of inferno. How the Afar people manage to live in
25 this place, and why they choose to, puzzles the rest of Ethiopia, as it does me.

"But," said Solomon, scratching one of the small fly-bites that were troubling all of us, "if we could return here in 50 years, this village would be different. There will be streets, electricity, and proper buildings. As Ethiopia modernises, places like this will be made more comfortable for people. Hamed Ela will probably be a big town."

30 And that is where Solomon was wrong. As Ethiopia modernises, the Afar will leave their desert home. They will drift into the towns and cities in the highlands. Their voracious herds of goats will die. Their camels will no longer be of any use. The only remembrance this place will have of the humans it bred will be the stone fittings of their flimsy, ruined stick huts, and the mysterious black rock burial mounds that litter the
35 landscape.

There is no modern reason for human beings to live in such places. Their produce is pitiful, the climate brutal and the distances immense. Salt is already produced as cheaply by industrial means. If market forces don't kill the trade, the conscience of the animal rights movement will, for the laden camels suffer horribly on their journey. The
40 day is coming when camels will go down there no more. In fifty years the Danakil will be a national park, visited by rubbernecking tourists in helicopters. Camels will be found in zoos. Goats will be on their way to elimination from every ecologically fragile part of the planet.

Even in America, deserts are not properly inhabited any more. Unreal places such as
45 Las Vegas have sprung up where people live in an air-conditioned and artificially
irrigated bubble, but the land itself is emptier than before. Tribes who were part of the
land, and lived off it, have mostly gone, their descendants living in reservations. The
wilderness places of North America are vast and exceptionally well preserved; but they
are not part of many people's lives, except those of tourists. We are becoming outsiders
50 to the natural world, watching it on the Discovery Channel.

Those who call themselves environmentalists celebrate this. "Leave nothing and take
nothing away," read the signs at the gates of nature reserves. Practical advice, perhaps,
but is there not something melancholy in what that says about modern man's desired
relationship with nature? Will we one day confine ourselves to watching large parts of
55 our planet only from observation towers?

I have no argument against the international development movement that wants to see
the Afars in clean houses with running water and electrical power, and schools, and a
clinic nearby—away, in other words, from their gruesome desert life. All this is
inevitable.

60 But as that new way of living arrives—as we retreat from the wild places, and the fences
of national parks go up; as we cease the exploitation of animals, and the cow, the camel,
the sheep, the chicken and the pig become items in modern exhibition farms, where
schoolchildren see how mankind used to live; as our direct contact with our fellow
creatures is restricted to zoos, pets and fish tanks; and as every area of natural beauty is
65 set about with preservation orders and rules to keep human interference to a
minimum—will we not be separating ourselves from our planet in order, as we suppose,
to look after it better? Will we not be loving nature, but leaving it?

They say there is less traffic across the Sahara today than at any time in human history,
even if you include motor transport. The great days of camel caravans are over. As for
70 the inhabitants, the nomads are on a path to extinction as a culture. Nomadic life does
not fit the pattern of nation states, taxes, frontiers and controls. And though for them
there is now government encouragement to stay, their culture is doomed. Amid the
indescribable majesty of this place—the crumbling towers of black rock, the scream of
the jackal, the waterless canyons, yellow dunes, grey plateaus and purple thorn
75 bushes—I have felt like a visitor to a monumental ruin, walked by ghosts. There are
fragments of pottery, thousands of cave paintings of deer, giraffe, elephant, and men in
feathers, dancing . . . but no people, not a soul.

In the beginning, man is expelled from the Garden of Eden. In the end, perhaps, we
shall leave it of our own accord, closing the gate behind us.

From *The Times,* February 25, 2006 (slightly adapted)

QUESTIONS

Marks Code

1. What is surprising about the writer's **word choice** in the first sentence? 2 A

2. Why does the writer add the expression "we suppose" (line 3) to the sentence here? 1 U

3. The word "floes" (line 6) usually refers to icebergs.

   Explain how it is appropriate to use it as a metaphor to refer to the appearance of the rock salt deposits. 2 A/E

4. Explain how any **one** example of the writer's choice of descriptive detail in lines 10–12 emphasises the hardships of the journey. 1 A

5. Explain **in your own words** the contrasting impressions the writer has of the village in Hamed Ela (see lines 18–19). 2 U

6. Explain what the word "fumed" (line 22) suggests about the volcano, apart from having smoke coming from it. 1 U

7. Explain why the sentence "And that is where Solomon was wrong" (line 30) is an effective link between the paragraphs contained in lines 26 to 35. 2 E

8. What does the word "drift" suggest about how "the Afar will leave their desert home" (lines 30–31)? 1 U

9. The writer tells us "There is no modern reason for human beings to live in such places" (line 36).

   Explain **in your own words two** reasons why this is the case.

   Look in the next three sentences (lines 36–39) for your answer. 2 U

10. Explain fully the appropriateness of the **word choice** of "rubbernecking tourists in helicopters" (line 41). 2 A

11. Explain how the writer develops the idea of Las Vegas being "Unreal" (line 44). 2 A

12. Explain why the expression "watching it on the Discovery Channel" (line 50) effectively illustrates our relationship with "wilderness places". 2 E

13. What is the effect of the writer's inclusion of the words "Those who call themselves" in the sentence beginning in line 51? 1 U

14. What is the **tone** of the two sentences in lines 52–55? 1 A

15. Explain how other words in lines 56–58 help us to work out the meaning or sense of "gruesome desert life". 2 U

16. Look at lines 60–67.

    (a) Identify any feature of **sentence structure** the writer uses effectively in this paragraph. 1 A

    (b) Show how your chosen feature helps to clarify or support the writer's argument. 2 A

17. Explain **in your own words** why "the nomads are on a path to extinction as a culture" (line 70). 1 U

18. Explain any reason why the final paragraph (lines 78–79) works well as a conclusion to the passage. 2 E

Total (30)

[END OF QUESTION PAPER]

X115/202

NATIONAL
QUALIFICATIONS
2008

THURSDAY, 15 MAY
2.20 PM – 3.50 PM

ENGLISH
INTERMEDIATE 2
Critical Essay

Answer **two** questions.

Each question must be taken from a different section.

Each question is worth 25 marks.

SQA

Answer TWO questions from this paper.

Each question must be chosen from a different Section (A–E). You are not allowed to choose two questions from the same Section.

In all Sections you may use Scottish texts.

Write the number of each question in the margin of your answer booklet and begin each essay on a fresh page.

You should spend about 45 minutes on each essay.

The following will be assessed:

- **the relevance of your essays to the questions you have chosen**

- **your knowledge and understanding of key elements, central concerns and significant details of the chosen texts**

- **your explanation of ways in which aspects of structure/style/language contribute to the meaning/effect/impact of the chosen texts**

- **your evaluation of the effectiveness of the chosen texts, supported by detailed and relevant evidence**

- **the quality and technical accuracy of your writing.**

Each question is worth 25 marks. The total for this paper is 50 marks.

SECTION A—DRAMA

Answers to questions in this section should refer to the text and to such relevant features as: characterisation, key scene(s), structure, climax, theme, plot, conflict, setting . . .

1. Choose a play in which there is a significant conflict between two characters.

   Describe the conflict and show how it is important to the development of the characterisation and theme of the play.

2. Choose a play which has a tragic ending.

   Show how the ending of the play results from the strengths and/or weaknesses of the main character(s).

3. Choose a play in which a character encounters difficulties within the community in which he or she lives.

   Show how the character copes with the difficulties he or she encounters and how his or her actions contribute to the theme of the play.

SECTION B—PROSE

Answers to questions in this section should refer to the text and to such relevant features as: characterisation, setting, language, key incident(s), climax/turning point, plot, structure, narrative technique, theme, ideas, description . . .

4. Choose a novel **or** short story which has a turning point or moment of realisation for at least one of the characters.

   Briefly describe what has led up to the turning point or moment. Go on to show what impact this has on the character(s) and how it affects the outcome of the novel or story.

5. Choose a novel **or** short story in which you feel sympathy with one of the main characters because of the difficulties or injustice or hardships she or he has to face.

   Describe the problems the character faces and show by what means you are made to feel sympathy for her or him.

6. Choose a non-fiction text **or** group of texts which uses setting, **or** humour, **or** description to make clear to you an interesting aspect of a society.

   Show how the use of any of these techniques helped you to understand the writer's point of view on the interesting aspect of this society.

SECTION C—POETRY

Answers to questions in this section should refer to the text and to such relevant features as: word choice, tone, imagery, structure, content, rhythm, theme, sound, ideas . . .

7. Choose a poem which creates an atmosphere of sadness, pity, or loss.

   Show how the poet creates the atmosphere and what effect it has on your response to the subject matter of the poem.

8. Choose a poem about a strong relationship—for example, between two people, or between a person and a place.

   Show how the poet, by the choice of content and the skilful use of techniques, helps you to appreciate the strength of the relationship.

9. Choose a poem which reflects on an aspect of human behaviour in such a way as to deepen your understanding of human nature.

   Describe the aspect of human behaviour which you have identified and show how the poet's use of ideas and techniques brought you to a deeper understanding of human nature.

[Turn over

SECTION D—FILM AND TV DRAMA

> *Answers to questions in this section should refer to the text and to such relevant features as: use of camera, key sequence, characterisation, mise-en-scène, editing, setting, music/sound effects, plot, dialogue . . .*

10. Choose a film or TV drama* which involves the pursuit of power or the fulfilment of an ambition.

    Show how the theme is developed through the presentation of character and setting.

11. Choose an opening sequence from a film which effectively holds your interest and makes you want to watch the rest of the film.

    Show what elements of the opening sequence have this effect, and how they relate to the film as a whole.

12. Choose a film or TV drama* which reflects an important aspect of society.

    Describe the aspect of society being dealt with and show how the techniques used by the film or programme maker help to deepen your understanding of the importance of this aspect.

* "TV drama" includes a single play, a series or a serial.

SECTION E—LANGUAGE

> *Answers to questions in this section should refer to the text and to such relevant features as: register, accent, dialect, slang, jargon, vocabulary, tone, abbreviation . . .*

13. Consider the language of advertising.

    In any one advertisement identify the ways in which language is used successfully. Explain what it is about these usages which makes them effective.

14. Consider the language of any form of modern electronic communication.

    Identify some features of this language which differ from normal usage and say how effective you think these features are in communicating information.

15. Consider the distinctive language of any specific group of people.

    What aspects of the group's language are distinctive and what advantage does the group gain from the use of such language?

[END OF QUESTION PAPER]

2009

[BLANK PAGE]

X115/201

NATIONAL QUALIFICATIONS 2009	FRIDAY, 15 MAY 1.00 PM – 2.00 PM	ENGLISH INTERMEDIATE 2 Close Reading

Answer all questions.

30 marks are allocated to this paper.

Read the passage carefully and then answer **all** the questions, **using your own words as far as possible**.

The questions will ask you to show that:

you understand the main ideas and important details in the passage—in other words, **what** the writer has said (**Understanding–U**);

you can identify, using appropriate terms, the techniques the writer has used to get across these ideas—in other words, **how** he has said it (**Analysis–A**);

you can, using appropriate evidence, comment on how effective the writer has been—in other words, **how well** he has said it (**Evaluation–E**).

A code letter (U, A, E) is used alongside each question to identify its purpose for you. The number of marks attached to each question will give some indication of the length of answer required.

Why Dickens was the hero of Soweto

In this passage, the writer informs us about the effect that books by Charles Dickens, a 19th-century English writer, had on black South African children during the time of racial segregation ("apartheid") in South Africa. "Afrikaans" was the form of Dutch spoken in South Africa by some white rulers before the arrival of democracy in that country.

Hector Pieterson was 12 when he died. Today a museum bearing his name commemorates his death—and hundreds of others—which occurred some 30 years ago at a place whose name has come to symbolise uprising against oppression: Soweto.

Hector was one of thousands of black children who took to the streets on June 16, 1976,
5 in protest about schooling under the apartheid regime in South Africa. When police opened fire on the march it brought the word Soweto to the attention of the world. But less well known is the role that Charles Dickens played in events.

The march was in protest at a government edict making Afrikaans compulsory in schools. From January 1976, half of all subjects were to be taught in it, including ones in
10 which difficulties of translation were often an issue.

To pupils accustomed to being educated in English, the Afrikaans policy was the last of a line of insults delivered in the name of "Bantu" or "native education". They thought being taught in Afrikaans, the language of a regime that had tried to "unpeople" them, would cost them their last remaining freedom—that of thinking for themselves, using
15 their minds.

That is where Dickens came in. Many books were banned under apartheid but not the classics of English literature. Pupils arriving hungry at school every day were captivated by the story of a frail but courageous boy named Oliver Twist.

The book was a revelation. Systemised oppression of children happened in England too!
20 They were not alone. Slave labour, thin rations and cruel taunts were part of a child's life in the world outside as well.

One former pupil, now in his forties, says of Dickens: "Four or five of us would be together and discuss the stories. And to think he wasn't banned! The authorities didn't know what was in these books, how they helped us to be strong, to think that we were
25 not forgotten."

Not being forgotten was particularly crucial. The apartheid regime had tried to "vanish" black people. Feeling abandoned and isolated, people turned to Dickens as someone who understood their plight.

But there were not enough books to go round. Few of the crateloads of Shakespeare,
30 Hardy and Dickens shipped from Britain reached the townships. Instead, they came to Soweto in parcels from charities. They were read by candlelight, often out loud, shared in a circle, or passed from hand to hand.

At Morris Isaacson School, one of the moving forces behind the Soweto protest, which produced two of its leaders, Murphy Morobe, "Shakespeare's best friend in Africa", and
35 Tsietsi Mashinini, there were 1,500 pupils and three copies of *Oliver Twist* in 1976. The former pupils recall waiting months for their turn, with a similar wait for *Nicholas Nickleby*.

But it was Oliver that they took to heart: students at one of the country's leading black colleges, Lovedale, formed a committee to ask for more.

40 Calling it the Board, after Dickens's Board of Guardians, they asked for more lessons, more food—and more and better books. Their reward was to be charged with public violence. All 152 "board" members were expelled from the college and some were jailed.

They felt that Dickens was obviously on their side. Descriptions of Gamfield's "ugly leer" and Bumble's "repulsive countenance" and Oliver being beaten by Mrs
45 Sowerberry and shoved "but nothing daunted" into the dust-cellar were evidence that this English author understood the plight of black South Africans.

Dickens's compassion for the poor linked the people of Soweto to a worldwide literature of tremendous importance.

The veteran South African trumpeter Hugh Masekela later chose *Nicholas Nickleby* as
50 his favourite book on a popular radio programme, *Desert Island Discs*, telling the presenter what its author did for people in the townships: "He taught us suffering is the same everywhere."

The love of books that enabled an author dead for more than 100 years to inspire thousands of schoolchildren came mainly from grandmothers who had educated their
55 families orally, then urged them to read widely and learn all that they could.

It also came from people such as the activist Steve Biko, whose own mentor, the Brazilian educator Paulo Freire, spent a lifetime working with forest people who had no formal education, teaching them to "name the world their own way".

That is what the youth of Soweto wanted—a future in their own words. And they got it.

60 "Africans are not dustbins," declared some of the June 16 placards; and "Beware of Afrikaans, the most dangerous drug for our future." By the following year, the language had been withdrawn from classrooms as unworkable. And so, thanks to the influence of a long-dead British author, the sacrifices of Hector Pieterson and many other Africans have proved to be not entirely in vain —which Dickens himself would surely applaud.

Adapted from an article by Carol Lee in *The Times*, 10th June, 2006

QUESTIONS

Marks Code

1. Explain fully any way in which the writer makes the opening paragraph dramatic.   2 A

2. The writer tells us that Soweto "has come to symbolise uprising against oppression" (line 3).

   Write down one expression from the next paragraph (lines 4–7) which continues the idea of uprising, **and** one which continues the idea of oppression.   2 U

3. Explain **in your own words**

   (a) what the marchers were objecting to, according to lines 8–10;   2 U

   (b) why this issue was so important to them, according to lines 11–15.   1 U

4. Look at lines 16–25.

   (a) Explain **in your own words** why Dickens's books were not "banned under apartheid" (line 16).   1 U

   (b) **In your own words** explain why Dickens's book *Oliver Twist* would have "captivated" the Soweto children.   2 U

5. Explain the purpose of the exclamation mark in line 23.   1 A

6. "But there were not enough books to go round." (line 29)

   (a) Explain how this sentence provides a link between paragraphs at this point.   2 A

   (b) Explain fully how the paragraph between lines 33 and 37 illustrates the idea that there were not enough books to go round.   2 A

7. Explain why the writer's use of "reward" in line 41 is ironic.   2 A

8. Explain why the writer's use of examples from the writing of Dickens in lines 43 to 46 is effective in advancing her argument at this point.   3 E

9. Look at lines 49–52.

   Explain **in your own words** why Hugh Masekela thought Dickens was so important.   2 U

10. Explain **in your own words** how the grandmothers referred to in line 54 instilled a love of books in their grandchildren.   2 U

11. Explain how any aspect of the **structure** of the paragraph in line 59 contributes to its effectiveness.   2 A

12. Look at the placard text "Beware of Afrikaans, the most dangerous drug for our future". (lines 60–61)

    Explain why this expression is an effective image or metaphor.   2 A/E

13. Look at the last paragraph of the passage (lines 60–64).

    Explain fully why this provides an effective conclusion to the passage.   2 A/E

Total (30)

[END OF QUESTION PAPER]

X115/202

NATIONAL
QUALIFICATIONS
2009

FRIDAY, 15 MAY
2.20 PM – 3.50 PM

ENGLISH
INTERMEDIATE 2
Critical Essay

Answer **two** questions.

Each question must be taken from a different section.

Each question is worth 25 marks.

XSQA

Answer TWO questions from this paper.

Each question must be chosen from a different Section (A–E). You are not allowed to choose two questions from the same Section.

In all Sections you may use Scottish texts.

Write the number of each question in the margin of your answer booklet and begin each essay on a fresh page.

You should spend about 45 minutes on each essay.

The following will be assessed:

- **the relevance of your essays to the questions you have chosen**
- **your knowledge and understanding of key elements, central concerns and significant details of the chosen texts**
- **your explanation of ways in which aspects of structure/style/language contribute to the meaning/effect/impact of the chosen texts**
- **your evaluation of the effectiveness of the chosen texts, supported by detailed and relevant evidence**
- **the quality and technical accuracy of your writing.**

Each question is worth 25 marks. The total for this paper is 50 marks.

SECTION A—DRAMA

Answers to questions in this section should refer to the text and to such relevant features as: characterisation, key scene(s), structure, climax, theme, plot, conflict, setting . . .

1. Choose a character from a play whose fate is unfortunate or unhappy.

   Show how much of the character's misfortune is caused by the personality and decisions of the character and how much by other circumstances in the play.

2. Choose a scene from a play in which suspense or tension is built up.

   Show how this suspense or tension is built up and what effect this scene has on the play as a whole.

3. Choose a play which deals with a close relationship within a family or a community.

   Show how the portrayal of the relationship helps in your understanding of the central concerns of the play.

SECTION B—PROSE

Answers to questions in this section should refer to the text and to such relevant features as: characterisation, setting, language, key incident(s), climax/turning point, plot, structure, narrative technique, theme, ideas, description . . .

4. Choose a novel **or** a short story in which a character is in conflict with his or her friends or relatives or society.

   Show how the conflict arises and what effect it has on the character's fate in the novel or short story as a whole.

5. Choose a novel **or** a short story which deals with the effects of evil or war or deceit or a breakdown in society or a breakdown in relationship(s).

   Show how any of these negative pressures affects the main character in the novel or short story and go on to show whether or not she or he tackles it successfully.

6. Choose a **non-fiction** text **or** group of texts which interests you because of its detailed and vivid description of scenes, events, people.

   Show how the detailed description makes the scenes, events, people vivid for you and increases your understanding of what is happening.

SECTION C—POETRY

Answers to questions in this section should refer to the text and to such relevant features as: word choice, tone, imagery, structure, content, rhythm, theme, sound, ideas . . .

7. Choose a poem which deals with childhood, adolescence, family life or old age.

   Show how the poet deepens your understanding of any of these stages of life by the choice of content and the skilful use of poetic techniques.

8. Choose a poem which deals with a particular time of year or a particular place.

   Show how the poet, by his or her choice of content and style, persuades you to adopt his or her view of the season or the place.

9. Choose a poem which has as one of its central concerns a personal, social or religious issue.

   Show how the content and the poetic techniques used increase your understanding of the issue.

[Turn over

SECTION D—FILM AND TV DRAMA

> *Answers to questions in this section should refer to the text and to such relevant features as: use of camera, key sequence, characterisation, mise-en-scène, editing, setting, music/sound effects, plot, dialogue . . .*

10. Choose a film **or** TV drama* which both entertains and helps to raise awareness of social issues.

    Show how the film or TV drama you have chosen succeeds in both these aspects.

11. Choose a sequence from a film which is important both to the atmosphere and to the plot of the film.

    Show how atmosphere is created in the sequence and go on to show how the sequence and the atmosphere are important to the film as a whole.

12. Choose a film **or** TV drama* which is set **either** in a past age **or** in the future.

    Show how the director/programme-maker has created the setting of the past **or** the future and go on to show how the setting increases your enjoyment of the film or TV drama.

    * "TV drama" includes a single play, a series or a serial.

SECTION E—LANGUAGE

> *Answers to questions in this section should refer to the text and to such relevant features as: register, accent, dialect, slang, jargon, vocabulary, tone, abbreviation . . .*

13. Consider how TV programmes aimed at young audiences have an effect on the language young people use.

    Identify any recent changes in vocabulary or accent that you are aware of and explain whether you feel the new words/accents are more effective in communicating than those which they have replaced.

14. Consider the use of emotive language in any form of advertising with which you are familiar.

    By referring to specific examples show how effective you feel the use of emotive language is in its particular context.

15. Consider the distinctive language found in any group of people with a shared interest in a sport, hobby, job or activity.

    By referring to specific examples of distinctive vocabulary or codes or grammatical forms show whether or not these features increase the effectiveness of communication within the group.

[END OF QUESTION PAPER]

2010

[BLANK PAGE]

X115/201

NATIONAL QUALIFICATIONS 2010	THURSDAY, 13 MAY 1.00 PM – 2.00 PM	ENGLISH INTERMEDIATE 2 Close Reading

Answer all questions.

30 marks are allocated to this paper.

Read the passage carefully and then answer **all** the questions, **using your own words as far as possible**.

The questions will ask you to show that:

you understand the main ideas and important details in the passage—in other words, **what** the writer has said (**Understanding—U**);

you can identify, using appropriate terms, the techniques the writer has used to get across these ideas—in other words, **how** he has said it (**Analysis—A**);

you can, using appropriate evidence, comment on how effective the writer has been—in other words, **how well** he has said it (**Evaluation—E**).

A code letter (U, A, E) is used alongside each question to identify its purpose for you. The number of marks attached to each question will give some indication of the length of answer required.

The Mighty Qin

This piece was written round about the time that an exhibition of some of the warriors from the ancient Chinese Terracotta Army was on display in the British Museum in London.

Qin Shi Who? My reaction entirely. I had heard of the Terracotta Army, of course. I had even seen some of them when a vanguard of warriors came to London in the 1980s. But I couldn't have told you who Qin Shihuangdi (pronounced *Chin Shur Hwang Dee*) was. Even if you'd said he was the First Emperor of China, I'd have had only the haziest
5 recollection of what you were talking about.

That probably goes for the vast majority of people in the West. And given that he is one of the most colossal figures ever to have walked the earth, that is rather shocking. For Qin Shihuangdi, its First Emperor, created China more than two millennia ago, establishing the world's longest-lasting empire. A visionary, a brutal tyrant and a
10 megalomaniac, he is the greatest historical figure that most of us have never heard of.

I only began to grasp this a few months ago when I travelled to Xi'an to visit the First Emperor's mind-boggling mausoleum, home to his Terracotta Army. "This is one of the people who changed the world," said Neil MacGregor, director of the British Museum. "There are terribly few historical figures whose achievements lasted like that.
15 This is really one of the great, great figures in human history."

The written historical sources for the man who bequeathed his name to his country are scant. Born Ying Zheng in 259 BC, he was the son of the king of Qin, in central China. He succeeded at the age of 13 and there was a period when he ruled with a regent. Then, when he was properly established on the throne, he embarked on what was
20 China's only real revolution until the 20th century.

Through clever diplomacy and brilliant military strategy he conquered and subdued neighbouring states. He achieved this by developing a highly organised army. Qin chariots had an improved design of smaller wheels with more spokes that provided greater stability and durability. The width of axles was made uniform, a seemingly small
25 innovation with massive repercussions: the chariots could ride relatively smoothly down the same ruts in the road and so avoid churning up the entire highway. The light infantry were armed with extremely sharp bronze weapons and crossbows and supported by cavalry.

This formidable war machine brought the warring states under the control of Qin, and
30 the heart of the area that we now call China was united for the first time in 221 BC. Ying Zheng decided to mark the success by renaming himself Qin Shihuangdi, or First Emperor of Qin.

The first Emperor survived at least three assassination attempts in subsequent years, incidents that served to tighten his grip on every aspect of life. He created a surveillance
35 culture in which neighbours were expected to spy on each other and lived in fear of terrible punishments for failing to do so or for breaking the many laws. One of the most miserable punishments, which very often proved to be a death sentence, was to be dispatched into the wilderness to toil on the construction of the wall Qin Shihuangdi had ordered to be built along the northern frontier of the empire.

40 Although there had been a tradition of building walls to mark the boundaries of territory and keep neighbours out, the First Emperor's undertaking was the most significant building project to date, aiming to protect the borders from nomads. His wall was rather farther north than what we think of today as the Great Wall, which is the series of fortifications (not one single wall) built in the Ming Dynasty, which ruled China for

45 almost three centuries from 1368. Little of the Qin wall remains beyond a few mounds that are believed to be from the First Emperor's era. But he is regarded as the grandfather of the Great Wall, that iconic symbol of China's historical separateness and age-old industriousness.

The First Emperor's imprint on the lives of the inhabitants of his far-flung kingdoms
50 was seen further. He unified the script, demanding that all states write the pictographs of ancient Chinese in the same way. So, although the words might be pronounced differently in different parts of the empire, once they were written down everyone who could read could understand each other, a particular advantage for traders. Some of the pictographs are recognisable in the language today, and the principle of a single written
55 language that can be spoken in different ways remains.

But for the First Emperor, establishing complete control over his empire was not enough. He wanted to rule forever. If he couldn't have immortality in this world, the next best thing would be to rule in the nether world. We knew about his tomb mound because the ancient sources referred to it, and it has always been there.

60 The tomb itself may never be opened because of the sensitivities of disturbing the Emperor, although some archaeologists hope that improved technology may one day allow some form of exploration.

The ancient sources refer to 700,000 people labouring on the tomb, but make no reference to what else the Emperor had devised under the ground. This is presumably
65 because they didn't know about his subterranean empire, which lay undisturbed until 1974. Those of the 600 pits that have been examined have yielded almost 1,800 mass-produced clay figures with another 6,000 believed to exist. In this mountain fastness Qin Shihuangdi wanted an army to protect him from his enemies, but also wanted his civil servants on hand and musicians and acrobats to entertain him.

70 "I can't think of anyone else who had the scale of ambition to think of replicating their entire kingdom," says MacGregor. "Nobody else in human history has attempted to do that, and what is fascinating is that it's the eternal underground that has survived and nothing else. We have no buildings, we have no writings, this is all that survives. The people making the figures knew they were making them to serve the Emperor and live
75 forever. And in a funny way they have."

The Emperor went to his tomb rather earlier than he had intended. In 210 BC, on one of his imperial progresses, he fell ill and died in his carriage.

There is no substitute for seeing the mass ranks of the Terracotta Army. But the British Museum wants to do two things: show visitors a selection of warriors up close in a way
80 that is not possible in Xi'an, and tell the story of the man whose breathtaking megalomania gave us one of the wonders of the world. The telling of that story is long overdue.

Damian Whitworth in *The Times*

QUESTIONS   *Marks Code*

1. Looking in the opening paragraph (lines 1–5) for your answer, explain **in your own words** what the writer's original "reaction" to the name Qin Shihuangdi was.   1 U

2. The first paragraph (lines 1–5) is written in a chatty style. Identify **one** expression or feature from these lines which contributes to this chattiness, and explain why it does so.   2 A

3. Look at paragraph 2 (lines 6–10).

   Give **in your own words two** reasons why it is "rather shocking" that most people in the West do not know about Qin.   2 U

4. Show how any **one** feature of Neil MacGregor's word choice (see lines 12–15) makes it clear that he thinks of Qin as someone special.   2 A

5. Explain **in your own words two** of the consequences of the improvements Qin made to his war chariots (see lines 24–26).   2 U

6. How appropriate is the expression "formidable war machine" (line 29) at this point in the passage?   3 E

7. Explain **in your own words** any **two** ways in which Qin managed to "tighten his grip on every aspect of life" (line 34).   2 U

8. What does the writer gain by using "toil" (line 38) rather than the word "work"?   1 A

9. The writer calls the Great Wall an "iconic symbol" (line 47).

   (*a*) Why is it appropriate to call the wall a "symbol"?   1 A/E

   (*b*) **In your own words**, explain fully what aspects of China it symbolises.   3 U

10. Explain how the sentence "But for the First Emperor, establishing complete control over his empire was not enough." (lines 56–57) works as a link between paragraphs at this point.   2 A

11. Show fully how the writer introduces a **tone** of doubt when he writes about the prospects for opening the tomb (lines 60–62).   2 A

12. How does the writer convey the grandness or large scale of the tomb in lines 63–69? You should refer to technique as well as content.   2 A

13. Show how an aspect of what Neil MacGregor says (lines 70–75) effectively conveys his sense of wonder.

    Your answer should refer to an example of **word choice or structure**.   2 E

14. In what sense does the writer use "funny" in line 75?   1 U

15. Explain why any example of the **word choice** in the final paragraph (lines 78–82) contributes to a neat conclusion to the passage.   2 A

Total (30)

[END OF QUESTION PAPER]

X115/202

NATIONAL QUALIFICATIONS 2010	THURSDAY, 13 MAY 2.20 PM – 3.50 PM	ENGLISH INTERMEDIATE 2 Critical Essay

Answer **two** questions.

Each question must be taken from a different section.

Each question is worth 25 marks.

Answer TWO questions from this paper.

Each question must be chosen from a different Section (A–E). You are not allowed to choose two questions from the same Section.

In all Sections you may use Scottish texts.

Write the number of each question in the margin of your answer booklet and begin each essay on a fresh page.

You should spend about 45 minutes on each essay.

The following will be assessed:

- **the relevance of your essays to the questions you have chosen**

- **your knowledge and understanding of key elements, central concerns and significant details of the chosen texts**

- **your explanation of ways in which aspects of structure/style/language contribute to the meaning/effect/impact of the chosen texts**

- **your evaluation of the effectiveness of the chosen texts, supported by detailed and relevant evidence**

- **the quality and technical accuracy of your writing.**

Each question is worth 25 marks. The total for this paper is 50 marks.

SECTION A—DRAMA

Answers to questions in this section should refer to the text and to such relevant features as: characterisation, key scene(s), structure, climax, theme, plot, conflict, setting . . .

1. Choose a play in which a central character feels increasingly isolated from those around her or him.

   Explain why the character finds herself or himself isolated, and show what the consequences are for the character concerned.

2. Choose a scene from a play in which there is an important incident which leads to a turning point in the action.

   Explain what happens in the scene, and then go on to say how it affects the outcome of the play.

3. Choose a play in which one of the main concerns is love **or** jealousy **or** betrayal **or** reconciliation.

   Explain what the concern is, and show how it is explored throughout the play.

SECTION B—PROSE

Answers to questions in this section should refer to the text and to such relevant features as: characterisation, setting, language, key incident(s), climax, turning point, plot, structure, narrative technique, theme, ideas, description . . .

4. Choose a novel **or** a short story which gives you an insight into an aspect of human nature or behaviour.

   State what the aspect is, and show how the characters' actions and relationships lead you to a deeper understanding of human nature or behaviour.

5. Choose a novel **or** a short story with an ending which you find satisfactory.

   By looking at the novel or short story as a whole, explain why you find the ending satisfactory in bringing to a conclusion the main concerns of the text.

6. Choose a prose work (fiction **or** non-fiction) in which setting is an important feature.

   Explain how the writer creates the setting, and then go on to show how this feature contributes to your understanding of the text as a whole.

SECTION C—POETRY

Answers to questions in this section should refer to the text and to such relevant features as: word choice, tone, imagery, structure, content, rhythm, theme, sound, ideas . . .

7. Choose a poem which could be considered as having a powerful message.

   Show how the poet effectively conveys this message through his or her use of poetic techniques.

8. Choose a poem in which the poet creates a particular mood or atmosphere.

   Show how the poet creates this mood or atmosphere by his or her choice of subject matter and use of poetic techniques.

9. Choose a poem which portrays an interesting character.

   Show how the poet uses poetic techniques to make the character interesting.

[Turn over

SECTION D—FILM AND TV DRAMA

Answers to questions in this section should refer to the text and to such relevant features as: use of camera, key sequence, characterisation, mise-en-scène, editing, setting, music/sound, special effects, plot, dialogue . . .

10. Choose a film **or** TV drama* which deals with issues which mainly affect young people.

    Explain how the film or TV drama* deals with such issues, stating whether or not you find the portrayal of these issues realistic.

11. Choose a scene or sequence from a film or TV drama* which provides a climax to the action.

    Briefly describe the events leading up to the climax, and then explain how the techniques used by the film or programme makers create a heightened sense of importance in this scene or sequence.

12. Choose a film which you think is typical of its genre, for example: action, romance, comedy, horror . . .

    Explain how the film makers have used the features of the genre to create a successful film.

  * "TV drama" includes a single play, a series or a serial.

SECTION E—LANGUAGE

Answers to questions in this section should refer to the text and to such relevant features as: register, accent, dialect, slang, jargon, vocabulary, tone, abbreviation . . .

13. Consider a text which you find to be persuasive, for example: an advertisement, a speech, a newspaper article . . .

    By referring to specific examples from your chosen text, show how persuasive techniques have been used to convince you.

14. Consider the ways that young people use the internet to communicate and socialise, for example: networking sites, instant messaging, chat rooms, blogs . . .

    By referring to specific examples of language and vocabulary, explain how such communication differs from formal English, and what its attractions are for young people.

15. Consider the specialist language used by any group which has a common leisure, vocational or geographical connection.

    Show how the specialist language used by the group is effective in communicating shared interests accurately.

[END OF QUESTION PAPER]

[BLANK PAGE]

X270/201

NATIONAL
QUALIFICATIONS
2011

FRIDAY, 13 MAY
1.00 PM – 2.00 PM

ENGLISH
INTERMEDIATE 2
Close Reading

Answer all questions.

30 marks are allocated to this paper.

Read the passage carefully and then answer **all** the questions, **using your own words as far as possible**.

The questions will ask you to show that:

> you understand the main ideas and important details in the passage—in other words, **what** the writer has said (**Understanding—U**);

> you can identify, using appropriate terms, the techniques the writer has used to get across these ideas—in other words, **how** he has said it (**Analysis—A**);

> you can, using appropriate evidence, comment on how effective the writer has been—in other words, **how well** he has said it (**Evaluation—E**).

A code letter (U, A, E) is used alongside each question to identify its purpose for you. The number of marks attached to each question will give some indication of the length of answer required.

The gr8 db8

Some people say that text messaging is destroying the English language. David Crystal, an eminent professor of language, argues that it is not.

Recently, a newspaper article headed "I h8 txt msgs: how texting is wrecking our language" argued that texters are "vandals who are doing to our language what Genghis Khan did to his neighbours 800 years ago. They are destroying it: pillaging our punctuation; savaging our sentences."

5   As a new variety of language, texting has been condemned as "textese", "slanguage", a "digital virus", "bleak, bald, sad shorthand", "drab shrinktalk which masks dyslexia, poor spelling and mental laziness".

Ever since the arrival of printing—thought to be the invention of the devil because it would put false opinions into people's minds—people have been arguing that new
10 technology would have disastrous consequences for language. Scares accompanied the introduction of the telegraph, the telephone, and broadcasting. But has there ever been a linguistic phenomenon that has aroused such curiosity, suspicion, fear, confusion, antagonism, fascination, excitement and enthusiasm all at once as texting? And in such a short space of time. Less than a decade ago, hardly anyone had heard
15 of it.

People think that the written language seen on mobile phone screens is new and alien, but all the popular beliefs about texting are wrong. Its distinctiveness is not a new phenomenon, nor is its use restricted to the young. There is increasing evidence that it helps rather than hinders literacy. Texting has added a new dimension to language
20 use, but its long-term impact is negligible. It is not a disaster.

Research has made it clear that the early media hysteria about the novelty (and thus the dangers) of text messaging was misplaced. People seem to have swallowed whole the stories that youngsters use nothing else but abbreviations when they text, such as the reports that a teenager had written an essay so full of textspeak that her teacher
25 was unable to understand it. An extract was posted online, and quoted incessantly, but, as no one was ever able to track down the entire essay, it was probably a hoax.

There are several distinctive features of the way texts are written that combine to give the impression of novelty, but people have been initialising common phrases for ages. IOU is known from 1618. There is no real difference between a modern kid's "lol"
30 ("laughing out loud") and an earlier generation's "SWALK" ("sealed with a loving kiss").

English has had abbreviated words ever since it began to be written down. Words such as exam, vet, fridge and bus are so familiar that they have effectively become new words. When some of these abbreviated forms first came into use, they also
35 attracted criticism. In 1711, for example, Joseph Addison complained about the way words were being "miserably curtailed"—he mentioned pos (itive) and incog (nito).

Texters use deviant spellings—and they know they are deviant. But they are by no means the first to use such nonstandard forms as "cos" for "because" or "wot" for "what". Several of these are so much part of English literary tradition that they have
40 been given entries in the Oxford English Dictionary. "Cos" is there from 1828 and "wot" from 1829. Many can be found in the way dialect is written by such writers as Charles Dickens, Mark Twain, Walter Scott and D.H. Lawrence.

Sending a message on a mobile phone is not the most natural of ways to communicate. The keypad isn't linguistically sensible. No one took letter-frequency
45 considerations into account when designing it. For example, key 7 on my mobile contains four symbols, pqrs. It takes four key-presses to access the letter s, and yet s is one of the most frequently occurring letters in English. It is twice as easy to input q, which is one of the least frequently occurring letters. It should be the other way round. So any strategy that reduces the time and awkwardness of inputting graphic
50 symbols is bound to be attractive.

Abbreviations were used as a natural, intuitive response to a technological problem. And they appeared in next to no time. Texters simply transferred (and then embellished) what they had encountered in other settings. We have all left notes in which we have replaced "and" with "&", "three" with "3", and so on.

55 But the need to save time and energy is by no means the whole story of texting. When we look at some texts, they are linguistically quite complex. There are an extraordinary number of ways in which people play with language—creating riddles, solving crosswords, playing Scrabble, inventing new words. Professional writers do the same—providing catchy copy for advertising slogans, thinking up puns in
60 newspaper headlines, and writing poems, novels and plays. Children quickly learn that one of the most enjoyable things you can do with language is to play with its sounds, words, grammar—and spelling.

An extraordinary number of doom-laden prophecies have been made about the supposed linguistic evils unleashed by texting. Sadly, its creative potential has been
65 virtually ignored. But children could not be good at texting if they had not already developed considerable literacy awareness. Before you can write and play with abbreviated forms, you need to have a sense of how the sounds of your language relate to the letters. You need to know that there are such things as alternative spellings. If you are aware that your texting behaviour is different, you must have already realised
70 that there is such a thing as a standard.

Some people dislike texting. Some are bemused by it. But it is merely the latest manifestation of the human ability to be linguistically creative and to adapt language to suit the demands of diverse settings. There is no disaster pending. We will not see a new generation of adults growing up unable to write proper English. The language
75 as a whole will not decline. In texting what we are seeing, in a small way, is language in evolution.

Adapted from an article
by David Crystal in *The Guardian*

QUESTIONS   *Marks Code*

1. Look at the opening paragraph (lines 1–4).

    (*a*) Write down **one** expression from this paragraph which continues the idea
    introduced by "wrecking".   1   U

    (*b*) Identify a feature of the expression "pillaging our punctuation; savaging our
    sentences" which makes it effective.   1   A

2. The writer tells us that "texting has been condemned" (line 5).

    Explain fully how any **one** of the expressions he quotes in the rest of this
    paragraph conveys disapproval of text message language.   2   A

QUESTIONS (continued)   *Marks Cod*

3. Why does the writer mention "the telegraph, the telephone, and broadcasting" (line 11) at this point in his argument?   2 U

4. Look at the sentence "But . . . texting?" (lines 11–13).

   (a) In this sentence, what point is the writer making about attitudes to texting? 1 U

   (b) Show how the writer's **word choice or structure** helps to reinforce this point. 1 A

5. The writer tells us (line 17) that "all the popular beliefs about texting are wrong".

   Look at the remainder of the paragraph (lines 17–20), and then explain **in your own words** what **two** of these popular beliefs are.   2 U

6. How effective do you find the writer's use of "hysteria" (line 21) as an **image** or **metaphor**?   2 E

7. The expression "swallowed whole" (line 22) suggests that people were too ready to believe what they had heard.

   Show how the writer continues this idea of gullibility in the remainder of the paragraph.   2 A

8. Why is the writer correct when he tells us that "there is no real difference" between "lol" and "SWALK" (see lines 29–31)?   1 A

9. Re-read lines 32–36, and then explain **in your own words two** points the writer is making about abbreviations.   2 U

10. Explain how effective you find the author's inclusion of the names of Dickens, Twain, Scott and Lawrence (line 42).   2 E

11. Re-read lines 43–50, and then explain **in your own words** in what ways "The keypad isn't linguistically sensible".   2 U

12. Explain why the sentence "Abbreviations were used as a natural, intuitive response to a technological problem" (line 51) is an appropriate link at this point in the passage.   2 A

13. Explain fully why the writer's use of "But" (line 55) is appropriate at this point in the structure of his argument.   3 U/A

14. What **tone** does the writer create by using the expression "supposed linguistic evils" (line 64)?   1 A

15. Look at lines 65–70, and then explain briefly **and in your own words** what the writer means when he refers to "literacy awareness" (line 66).   1 U

16. Look at the final paragraph (lines 71–76), and then explain how well you feel this paragraph works as a conclusion to the passage as a whole.   2 E

Total (30)

[END OF QUESTION PAPER]

X270/202

NATIONAL
QUALIFICATIONS
2011

FRIDAY, 13 MAY
2.20 PM – 3.50 PM

ENGLISH
INTERMEDIATE 2
Critical Essay

Answer **two** questions.

Each question must be taken from a different section.

Each question is worth 25 marks.

XSQA

Answer TWO questions from this paper.

Each question must be chosen from a different Section (A–E). You are not allowed to choose two questions from the same Section.

In all Sections you may use Scottish texts.

Write the number of each question in the margin of your answer booklet and begin each essay on a fresh page.

You should spend about 45 minutes on each essay.

The following will be assessed:

- the relevance of your essays to the questions you have chosen
- your knowledge and understanding of key elements, central concerns and significant details of the chosen texts
- your explanation of ways in which aspects of structure/style/language contribute to the meaning/effect/impact of the chosen texts
- your evaluation of the effectiveness of the chosen texts, supported by detailed and relevant evidence
- the quality and technical accuracy of your writing.

Each question is worth 25 marks. The total for this paper is 50 marks.

SECTION A—DRAMA

Answers to questions in this section should refer to the text and to such relevant features as: characterisation, key scene(s), structure, climax, theme, plot, conflict, setting . . .

1. Choose a play in which there is a character who suffers from a human weakness such as ambition, selfishness, lack of self-knowledge, jealousy, pride, lust . . .

   Show how the weakness is revealed, then explain how this weakness affects both the characters and the events of the play.

2. Choose a play in which there is an important relationship between two of the main characters.

   Describe the nature of the relationship, and explain how it is developed throughout the play.

3. Choose a play which you feel has a dramatic final scene.

   Describe briefly what happens and explain how effective the ending is in bringing to a conclusion the central concerns of the text.

SECTION B—PROSE

> *Answers to questions in this section should refer to the text and to such relevant features as: characterisation, setting, language, key incident(s), climax, turning point, plot, structure, narrative technique, theme, ideas, description . . .*

4. Choose a novel **or** a short story in which you feel there is an incident of great importance to the story as a whole.

   Describe the incident and go on to show its importance to the development of the characters and the central concerns of the text.

5. Choose a novel **or** a short story which has a character who affects you emotionally.

   Describe how you feel about the character, and show how the writer leads you to feel this way.

6. Choose a prose work (fiction **or** non-fiction) in which the writer uses a memorable style/voice/narrative technique.

   Explain in detail how features of the writing style/voice/narrative technique contribute to the effectiveness of the text.

SECTION C—POETRY

> *Answers to questions in this section should refer to the text and to such relevant features as: word choice, tone, imagery, structure, content, rhythm, theme, sound, ideas . . .*

7. Choose a poem which deals with an important issue such as war, crime, poverty **or** racism.

   Explain how the poet deepens your understanding of the issue by the choice of content and the skilful use of poetic techniques.

8. Choose a poem which describes an animal **or** a place **or** an event in an effective way.

   Briefly state what is being described and go on to show how the techniques used in the poem make the description effective.

9. Choose a poem written in a specific form such as ballad, sonnet, elegy, monologue, ode . . .

   Explain how the distinctive features of this form contribute to your appreciation of the text.

[Turn over

SECTION D—FILM AND TV DRAMA

Answers to questions in this section should refer to the text and to such relevant features as: use of camera, key sequence, characterisation, mise-en-scène, editing, setting, music/sound, special effects, plot, dialogue . . .

10. Choose a film **or** TV drama* which has a character who could be described as a hero or as a villain.

    Explain how the the character is introduced and then developed throughout the film or TV drama.

11. Choose a film **or** TV drama* in which setting is an important feature.

    Explain how the setting is established and go on to show how the setting contributes to the effectiveness of the film **or** TV drama as a whole.

12. Choose a scene or sequence from a film **or** TV drama* in which an atmosphere of mystery, **or** horror, **or** suspense is created.

    Describe what happens in the scene or sequence, explaining how the techniques used by the film or programme makers create this atmosphere.

   * "TV drama" includes a single play, a series or a serial.

SECTION E—LANGUAGE

Answers to questions in this section should refer to the text and to such relevant features as: register, accent, dialect, slang, jargon, vocabulary, tone, abbreviation . . .

13. Consider a text which aims to persuade people to support a particular group, **or** to buy a particular product.

    By referring to specific examples from your chosen text, show how persuasive techniques are used.

14. Consider a modern form of communication such as e-mail **or** text message.

    By referring to specific examples of language and vocabulary, explain how such communication differs from formal English, and what advantages this presents to users.

15. Consider the specialist language used by any group of people to talk about a particular interest, for example, a sport, a job, a hobby . . .

    By referring to specific examples, show how the specialist language used by the group is effective in communicating ideas clearly.

[END OF QUESTION PAPER]

[BLANK PAGE]

X270/11/01

NATIONAL QUALIFICATIONS 2012	WEDNESDAY, 16 MAY 1.00 PM – 2.00 PM	ENGLISH INTERMEDIATE 2 Close Reading

Answer all questions.

30 marks are allocated to this paper.

Read the passage carefully and then answer **all** the questions, **using your own words as far as possible**.

The questions will ask you to show that:

> you understand the main ideas and important details in the passage—in other words, **what** the writer has said (**Understanding—U**);

> you can identify, using appropriate terms, the techniques the writer has used to get across these ideas—in other words, **how** he has said it (**Analysis—A**);

> you can, using appropriate evidence, comment on how effective the writer has been—in other words, **how well** he has said it (**Evaluation—E**).

A code letter (U, A, E) is used alongside each question to identify its purpose for you. The number of marks attached to each question will give some indication of the length of answer required.

SUPERSTITION

In this passage, the writer explores how superstition can both help and hinder us.

Tennis players are a funny bunch. Have you noticed how they always ask for three balls instead of two; how they bounce the ball the same number of times before serving, as if any deviation from their routine might bring the world collapsing on their heads?

5   But the superstitions and rituals so beloved by the world's top players are not confined to the court. They take even more bizarre twists when the poor dears get home after their matches. Goran Ivanisevic got it into his head that if he won a match he had to repeat everything he did the previous day, such as eating the same food at the same restaurant, talking to the same people and watching the same TV programmes. One year this meant that he had to watch Teletubbies every morning during his Wimbledon
10   campaign. "Sometimes it got very boring," he said.

Could it be that these multifarious superstitions tell us something of deeper importance not only about humanity but about other species on the planet?

The answer, I think, is to be found in the world of pigeons. Yes, really. These feathered fellows, you see, are the tennis players of the bird world. Don't take my word for it:
15   that was the opinion of B. F. Skinner, the man widely regarded as the father of modern psychology.

Skinner's view was based on a groundbreaking experiment that he carried out in 1947 in which he placed some hungry pigeons in a cage attached to an automatic mechanism that delivered food "at regular intervals with no reference whatsoever to the bird's
20   behaviour". He discovered that the pigeons associated the delivery of the food with whatever chance actions they happened to be performing at the moment it was first delivered. So what did the pigeons do? They kept performing the same actions, even though they had no effect whatsoever on the release of food.

I know, I know. This is nothing compared with the weird behaviour that goes on
25   at Wimbledon, but do you see the connection? The pigeons were acting as if they could influence the mechanism delivering the Trill in just the same way that Ivanisevic thought that he could influence the outcome of his next match by watching Teletubbies. To put it a tad formally, they both witnessed a random connection between a particular kind of behaviour and a desired outcome, and then (wrongly) inferred that one caused
30   the other.

But did Ivanisevic really believe that his superstitions were effective or was he just having us on? Well, let's hear from the man himself – this is what he said when asked if he had ever abandoned a ritual when it stopped working: "I didn't. They do work. I won Wimbledon." So, he really did believe. And what of the pigeons? They were,
35   unfortunately, unavailable for interview.

Superstitious behaviour emerged quite early in evolutionary history. What is certain is that it is widespread, particularly within *homo sapiens*. More than half of Americans admitted to being superstitious in a recent poll, and it is not just silly and gullible types either. At Harvard University, students frequently rub the foot of the statue of John
40   Harvard for good luck.

Even cricketers, perhaps the brightest and most sensible sportsmen of all (well, that's what they tell us), are not immune to superstition. Jack Russell, the former England wicketkeeper, was among the most notorious, refusing to change his hat or wicketkeeping

pads throughout his career, even though they became threadbare and smelly, something
45 that really got up the noses of his team-mates.

But this raises another, deeper question: why do so many of us maintain rituals of various kinds when they have no real connection with the desired outcome? Or, to put it another way, why is superstitious behaviour so widespread, not just within our species but beyond, when it seems to confer no tangible benefits? It's here that things get really
50 interesting (and just a little complex). And, as with most interesting things, the answer is to be found in deep evolutionary history.

Imagine a caveman going to pick some berries from some bushes near his rocky abode. He hears some rustling in the bushes and wrongly infers that there is a lion lurking in there and scarpers. He even gets a little superstitious about those bushes and gives them
55 a wide berth in future. Is this superstition a problem to our caveman? Well, not if there are plenty of other berry-bearing bushes from which to get his five-a-day.

But suppose that there really is a lion living in those bushes. The caveman's behaviour now looks not only sensible but life-saving. So, a tendency to perceive connections that do not actually exist can confer huge evolutionary benefits, providing a cocoon of safety
60 in a turbulent and dangerous world. The only proviso (according to some devilishly complicated mathematics known as game theory) is this: your superstitions must not impose too much of a burden on those occasions when they are without foundation.

And this is almost precisely what superstitions look like in the modern world. Some believe in horoscopes, but few allow them to dictate their behaviour; some like to wear
65 the same lucky shoes to every job interview, but it is not as if wearing a different pair would improve their chances of success; some like to bounce the ball precisely seven times before serving at tennis, but although they are wrong to suppose that this ball-bouncing is implicated in their success, it does not harm their prospects (even if it irritates those of us watching).

70 It is only when a superstition begins to compromise our deeper goals and aspirations that we have moved along the spectrum of irrationality far enough to risk a diagnosis of obsessive compulsive disorder. Take Kolo Touré, the former Arsenal defender, who insists on being the last player to leave the dressing room after the half-time break. No real problem, you might think, except that when William Gallas, his team-mate, was
75 injured and needed treatment at half-time during a match, Touré stayed in the dressing room until Gallas had been treated, forcing Arsenal to start the second half with only nine players.

When a superstition that is supposed to help you actually hinders you, it is probably time to kick the ritual into touch. With a rabbit's foot, obviously.

Matthew Syed, in *The Times*

QUESTIONS   *Marks   Code*

1. Look at lines 1–3, and then explain **in your own words** what is meant by tennis players being "a funny bunch".   1   U

2. Consider the first two sentences of the second paragraph (lines 4–6), and then show how any example of the writer's **word choice** here reveals what his attitude to "top players" is.   2   U

QUESTIONS (continued)   *Marks* *Code*

3. Explain why the paragraph in lines 11 and 12 works well at this point as a link of the ideas in the passage.   2   A

4. Explain **in your own words** why the writer can feel confident about using B. F. Skinner (see line 15) to support his claims about pigeons.   1   U

5. Explain how effective you find the writer's use of the **image** or **metaphor** "groundbreaking" (line 17) to refer to Skinner's experiment.   1   E

6. Look at lines 24–30, and then explain fully and **in your own words** what "the connection" was.   3   U

7. What is the effect of the inclusion of the sentence "They were, unfortunately, unavailable for interview" (lines 34–35)?   1   A

8. Why does the writer include the reference to Harvard University (line 39)?   1   A

9. Explain the humour of "something that really got up the noses of his team-mates" (lines 44–45).   2   A

10. Look again at lines 52–56.

    (*a*) How do these lines relate to the ideas the writer presents in the previous paragraph?   2   A

    (*b*) What is surprising about the expression "to get his five-a-day" (line 56)?   2   A

11. Explain **in your own words** what the "huge evolutionary benefits" (line 59) of superstitions are.   2   U

12. Explain the writer's use of a colon in line 61.   1   A

13. Look again at lines 63–69, in which the writer examines the nature of superstition nowadays.

    (*a*) Explain **in your own words** the points the writer makes.   2   U

    (*b*) How does the **sentence structure** reinforce the ideas the writer is putting forward?   1   A

14. Explain how effective you find the word "spectrum" (line 71) as an **image** or **metaphor** to illustrate people's "irrationality".   2   E

15. Why does the writer include the anecdote about the footballer Kolo Touré (lines 72–77)?   2   A

16. How effective do you find any aspect of the final paragraph (lines 78–79) as a conclusion to the passage?

    Your answer might deal with such features as **word choice** or **tone**.   2   E

[END OF QUESTION PAPER]   **Total (30)**

X270/11/02

NATIONAL
QUALIFICATIONS
2012

WEDNESDAY, 16 MAY
2.20 PM – 3.50 PM

ENGLISH
INTERMEDIATE 2
Critical Essay

Answer **two** questions.

Each question must be taken from a different section.

Each question is worth 25 marks.

SQA

Answer TWO questions from this paper.

Each question must be chosen from a different Section (A–E). You are not allowed to choose two questions from the same Section.

In all Sections you may use Scottish texts.

Write the number of each question in the margin of your answer booklet and begin each essay on a fresh page.

You should spend about 45 minutes on each essay.

The following will be assessed:

- **the relevance of your essays to the questions you have chosen**

- **your knowledge and understanding of key elements, central concerns and significant details of the chosen texts**

- **your explanation of ways in which aspects of structure/style/language contribute to the meaning/effect/impact of the chosen texts**

- **your evaluation of the effectiveness of the chosen texts, supported by detailed and relevant evidence**

- **the quality and technical accuracy of your writing.**

Each question is worth 25 marks. The total for this paper is 50 marks.

SECTION A—DRAMA

Answers to questions in this section should refer to the text and to such relevant features as: characterisation, key scene(s), structure, climax, theme, plot, conflict, setting . . .

1. Choose a play in which there is conflict between two characters in a family **or** a group.

   Show how the conflict occurs and explain how it affects the characters and the events of the play.

2. Choose a play in which a main character's actions have a significant effect on the rest of the play.

   Show how this character's actions have affected the other characters **and/or** the outcome of the play.

3. Choose a play which has developed your understanding of an important human emotion such as love, hatred, jealousy **or** any other emotion.

   Show how this understanding has been developed through the playwright's use of dramatic techniques.

SECTION B—PROSE

> *Answers to questions in this section should refer to the text and to such relevant features as: characterisation, setting, language, key incident(s), climax, turning point, plot, structure, narrative technique, theme, ideas, description . . .*

4. Choose a novel **or** a short story where there is an incident which is a turning point crucial to the fate of the main character.

   Briefly describe what happens at this point and go on to explain why this is crucial to the fate of a main character.

5. Choose a novel **or** a short story in which setting in place **and/or** time is an important feature.

   Briefly describe the setting(s) and explain the importance of this feature to the story.

6. Choose a novel **or** a short story **or** a non-fiction text **or** group of texts which deals with an important human issue (such as the abuse of power, conflict between good and evil, loss of freedom or hatred between individuals or groups).

   Show how the author reveals the issue through the portrayal of people and events throughout the text, and show how your understanding of the issue has deepened.

SECTION C—POETRY

> *Answers to questions in this section should refer to the text and to such relevant features as: word choice, tone, imagery, structure, content, rhythm, theme, sound, ideas . . .*

7. Choose a poem which describes a person's experience.

   Explain how the poetic techniques used to describe the experience make the poem more interesting.

8. Choose a poem which arouses strong emotion in you.

   Describe how you feel about the poem, and explain how the poet leads you to feel this way.

9. Choose a poem in which the poet creates a particular mood **or** atmosphere.

   Show how the poet creates this mood **or** atmosphere by his or her choice of subject matter and use of poetic techniques.

[Turn over

SECTION D—FILM AND TV DRAMA

Answers to questions in this section should refer to the text and to such relevant features as: use of camera, key sequence, characterisation, mise-en-scène, editing, setting, music/sound, special effects, plot, dialogue . . .

10. Choose a film **or** TV drama* in which the main character is an individual for whom we feel sympathy.

   Show how media techniques are used to portray the character in such a way that we feel sympathy.

11. Choose a scene or sequence from a film **or** TV drama* which is particularly dramatic.

   Describe what happens in the scene or sequence, explaining how the film or programme makers effectively use techniques to create drama.

12. Choose a film **or** TV drama* in which there is a character who poses a threat to the main character.

   Show how media techniques are used to portray the character in such a way that the audience reacts against him/her and sees the threat which he/she poses.

   * "TV drama" includes a single play, a series or a serial.

SECTION E—LANGUAGE

Answers to questions in this section should refer to the text and to such relevant features as: register, accent, dialect, slang, jargon, vocabulary, tone, abbreviation . . .

13. Consider the language of advertisements aimed at young people.

   By discussing at least one such advertisement, identify the key features which vary from other types of advertising and explain why these features could appeal to young people.

14. Consider the language specific to a group with a shared hobby, job, interest **or** location.

   By giving examples of distinctive vocabulary **or** grammatical constructions, show how the group's language is different from that used by the general population and discuss the advantages to the group of using its specific language.

15. Consider the differences between written language and an aspect of spoken language which you have studied.

   Explain, with references to examples, the similarities and differences between the two forms of language you have studied and go on to show which features of spoken language you find most effective.

[END OF QUESTION PAPER]

[BLANK PAGE]

Acknowledgements

Permission has been sought from all relevant copyright holders and Bright Red Publishing is grateful for the use of the following:

The article 'We are outsiders to the natural world, preferring to watch it on Discovery' taken from The Times, 25 February 2006. Reproduced by permission of Matthew Parris (2008 Close Reading pages 2–3);

An extract from 'A Child Called Freedom' by Carol Lee, published by Century. Reprinted by permission of The Random House Group Ltd. (2009 Close Reading pages 2–3);

An extract from the article 'China's Colossus' by Damian Whitworth taken from The Times © The Times/NI Syndication August 30th 2007 (2010 Close Reading pages 2–3);

An extract from the article '2b or not 2b' by David Crystal from The Guardian, 5 June 2008. Originally from 'txtng: the gr8 db8' published by Oxford University Press, 2008 © David Crystal (2011 Close Reading pages 2–3);

The article 'Superstition' by Matthew Syed © The Times/NI Syndication 1st July 2009 (2012 Close Reading pages 2–3).

INTERMEDIATE 2 | ANSWER SECTION

ENGLISH INTERMEDIATE 2
CLOSE READING
2008

1. There is a contradiction in "hellish yet beautiful"

2. He is not/cannot be sure

3. *Any two from:*
- similarity in size
- similarity in colour
- similarity in shape
- contrast with surroundings

4. *Any one example from:*
- The camels drink only twice - we would expect more
- Walking at night - implies the heat of the day
- The camels have to carry their own fodder - an additional burden
- Straw to eat - not nutritious
- Dry bread/"only...bread, sugar and tea" - unappetising/unvaried/limited range and/or not nutritious

5. Gloss of "friendly"
eg welcoming/helpful/hospitable/kindly/nice

Gloss of "flyblown"
eg rickety/flimsy/ramshackle/makeshift/uncomfortable/ physically inhospitable/unhygienic/poor

6. Idea of personification
eg that it was angry/threatening/bad-tempered

7. "(And) that" refers back to his words in the previous paragraph (about progress/growth/improvement)

"was wrong" leads to (the rebuttal contained in) the rest of the paragraph
or comment on linking function of "And"

8. It will happen piecemeal/gradually/without purpose or direction or motive on the part of those who do it.

9. *Glosses of two from:*
- their produce is pitiful
eg what they turn out is minimal
- the climate (is) brutal
eg the weather is oppressive
- the distances (are) immense
eg they have to travel a very long way
- Salt is already produced as cheaply by industrial means
eg salt can be obtained equally, efficiently in other ways
- Market forces [will] kill the trade
eg economic factors will overcome them
- the conscience of the animal rights movement
eg people concerned with animal welfare will act against them

10. *Word choice:*
- "rubbernecking"
suggests insensitivity/ghoulishness
- "tourists"
suggests invasiveness/superficiality

- "helicopters"
suggests intrusive modernity
or detachment **or** (financial) contrast

11. *Any one example and comment from:*
- "sprung up"
suggests an unnatural speed of growth
- "air-conditioned"
illustrates the necessity of climate alteration/ modification/control
- "artificially"
relates to the idea of falseness
- "artificially irrigated"
illustrates the innate dryness/hostility/ uninhabitable quality of the place
- "bubble"
suggests its fragility/quality of being insulated from elsewhere

12. Just as seeing something on TV is removed from reality/involvement (idea of vicariousness)
So we are separated from/are removed from/are at a distance from/do not belong to these places (lack of interaction)

13. Suggests disagreement/cynicism

14. Sad/pessimistic/gloomy/resigned/regretful/ concerned

15. If they are "away from" (pleasant things such as) clean houses/running water/power/schools/adjacent clinic
Then the expression must mean a harsh/spartan/unpleasant/horrible/ghastly existence

16. (a) *Any one from:*
- use of parenthesis
- use of semi-colon
- repeated use of (clauses starting with) "as"/listing
- use of (negative) question(s)

(b) *Any two effects from:*

Feature	Effect
Use of parenthesis	Helps identify/ isolate/specify what the "new way of living" is
Semi-colon construction **or** use of "as" **or** listing	Gives idea of multiplicity and/or variety of ways we are moving away from wilderness
Use of (negative) question(s)	Creates doubt in reader's mind And/or questions wisdom of what we are doing And/or implies agreement with sense of argument

17. Their way of life does not (readily)/conform to (modern) rules and/or boundaries (idea of imposition and/or constriction).
(gloss of "does not fit the pattern of nation states, taxes, frontiers and controls")

18.
- Idea of garden of Eden
recaps idea of magnificence of place
- Idea of expulsion
recaps idea of man's desertion of this place
- "of our own accord"
recaps idea of the leaving being by choice
- "closing the gate behind us"
recaps idea of irreversibility of process
or

the references to the gates of nature reserves
or
contains an appropriate idea of closure
or
retreating from Nature
- Use of imagery
matches use of imagery elsewhere (identified)
- Melancholy tone
matches sombre tone of passage
- The balance of "In the beginning..." and "In the end..."
is neat per se
- The balance of "expelled" and "leave it of our own accord"
is neat per se

ENGLISH INTERMEDIATE 2
CRITICAL ESSAY
2008

Please see Critical Essay Marking Principles on pages 64–65.

ENGLISH INTERMEDIATE 2
CLOSE READING
2009

1. *Any one: quotation/reference, comment from:*
   The bluntness/brevity/content of the opening sentence; "hundreds of others" is emphasised by use of parenthesis; the use of the colon isolates or enforces the pause before "Soweto"; the positioning of "Soweto" gives a climactic effect

2. Uprising: "took to the streets"/"march"/"(in) protest"
   Oppression: "(under the) apartheid regime" (or "apartheid" or "regime" alone) or "opened fire"

3. (a) A Government rule/law/decree/statute/order (gloss of "edict") forcing teaching in Afrikaans/making it obligatory/enforced/required (gloss of "compulsory")

   (b) It was a threat to their self-esteem or identity (gloss of "unpeople")
   OR it was a threat to their (intellectual) independence (gloss of "thinking for themselves")
   OR it was the last straw (gloss of "the last of a line of insults")

4. (a) They were abiding/memorable/lasting/ageless
   OR they were masterpieces (gloss of "classics")
   OR the regime did not understand their content (gloss of "didn't know what was in these books")

   (b) *Any one from:*
   They identified with Oliver and/or the events portrayed in the book/
   Their lives were like/the same as Oliver's
   Because they too were subjugated/exploited (gloss of "oppression" or "slave labour")
   OR they too were underfed (gloss of "hungry" or "thin rations")
   OR the inference can be made that they too were in poor health (gloss of "frail")
   OR they too were brave (gloss of "courageous")
   OR they too were mocked (by oppressors) (gloss of "cruel taunts")

5. To complement or convey the idea of surprise or ridicule.

6. (a) "books" refers back to Dickens in previous paragraph ; "not enough" anticipates the idea of paucity/scarcity developed in the rest of the paragraph

   (b) The exact figures/"1500 pupils and three copies"/"waiting months for their turn" shows the contrast between demand and supply

7. A reward is normally pleasant but what happened to them was unpleasant
   OR
   What happened to them was unpleasant
   and so the term is incongruous/peculiar/strange/odd/poignant/sarcastic/sardonic

8. The references to the unfairness/brutality/ unattractiveness (addressing the idea of ugliness) and (brave) resistance (addressing the idea of being "nothing daunted"); (clearly) show (why the Africans felt) Dickens was on their side

9. He showed that pain/distress/misery/anguish (gloss of "suffering") was the same throughout the world/in all places/the world over (gloss of "everywhere")

10. They taught them by word of mouth (gloss of "orally") and then drove/pushed/encouraged (gloss of "urged") them to read.

11. The long and short sentences contrast
     OR the dash produces a (dramatic) delay
     OR the brevity of the second sentence produces impact
     OR the introduction of the second sentence with "And"
     produces impact

12. Just as drugs are harmful (in the long term) so Afrikaans has a
     (long-reaching) deleterious effect on the lives of the Sowetans

13. Answers must identify one aspect or feature of the final
     paragraph and link it to a relevant aspect or feature elsewhere
     in the passage eg
     There is recapitulation of previously-mentioned ideas such as
     that of Dickens being long dead
     There is relation back to the introductory 3 paragraphs in the
     reference to Afrikaans
     There is relation back to the introductory 2 paragraphs in the
     reference to the date
     There is a reprising of an idea in the opening in the reference
     to the death of Hector Pieterson
     There is recapitulation of the idea of optimism in the
     uplifting tone

ENGLISH INTERMEDIATE 2
CRITICAL ESSAY
2009

Please see Critical Essay Marking Principles on pages 64–65.

ENGLISH INTERMEDIATE 2
CLOSE READING
2010

1. He had never/barely heard of him/puzzlement

2.
Question (and response) Verbless sentence(s) (throwaway effect of) "of course" Informality of abbreviated verbs (Helpful) explanation of pronunciation Use of 2nd person Humour of (facetious) capital letter at "Who" Informal use of initial "But" Terminal preposition ("about")	Makes it more informal/friendlier/less intimidating OR is a feature of conversation/dialogue/engagement

3. *Any two from:*
    He is a very important person in history (gloss of "colossal" or "greatest");
    He set up/founded China (gloss of "created");
    He set up/founded an imperial dynasty (gloss of "First Emperor");
    His regime was the most permanent/durable/ prolonged (gloss of "long-lasting")

4.
Example	Analysis
changed the world	suggests large extent of influence
terribly few	conveys near-uniqueness
(whose achievements) lasted like that	suggests permanence of influence
Really	intensifies
"great"	shows attitude of high regard
repetition of "great, great"	emphasises

5. *Any two from:*
    Glosses of:

stability	eg firmness/solidity/ strength/steadiness/ balance
durability	eg toughness/long-lasting quality/sturdiness/ resilience
chariots could ride relatively smoothly (down the same ruts in the road)	eg progress (in channels/grooves/ furrows) was easy/easier
avoid churning up the entire highway	eg road was not made uneven/less smooth/harder to make progress on/not so damaged

6. It (neatly/succinctly) continues/sums
    up/reinforces/emphasises/alludes to the
    frightening/redoubtable/fearsome quality and the
    efficiency/competence/ruthlessness of the army

7. *Any two from:*
    Glosses of:

surveillance culture/spy	people watched/observed one another
terrible punishments	severe reprisals/penalties
Many laws	multiplicity of regulations/edicts/ rulings/instructions

8. It conveys the hardship/protractedness/drudgery of the work

9. (a) It represents/stands for/is (readily) recognisable as representative (of China)

(b)

Gloss of "historical" or "age-old"	eg long-standing
Gloss of "separateness"	eg isolation
Gloss of "industriousness"	eg capacity for hard work

10. "establishing complete control over his empire" refers back to preceding ideas (relating to dominance)
"was not enough" prepares us for upcoming reference (to other things he wanted to do or have)
"But" introduces contrast

11. *Any two points from:*
He uses "may"; twice; he uses "some archaeologists"
he uses "hope"; he uses "one day"; he uses "some form"

12.

Content	He refers to the large number of people involved in its construction OR the large number of pits OR the large number of artefacts found OR the possibility of many more OR the desire to have many servants etc. (paraphrase of last sentence) Generalised comment about large numbers acceptable
Technique	
Typography	he uses numerals (for impact)
Word choice	he uses "empire", which suggests size of construction OR he uses "army", which alludes to the large numbers of figures

One answer from each section needed for 2 marks

13.

word choice	"I can't think of anyone else"	(emphatically) conveys sense of uniqueness
	"scale of ambition"	(clearly) conveys size of imagination/ grandeur of plan
	"entire kingdom"	(clearly) conveys size of undertaking
	"Nobody else (in human history has attempted to do that)"	(emphatically) conveys sense of uniqueness/rareness
	"fascinating"	(clearly) suggests the captivating nature of (this aspect of) the story
structure	repetition of "anyone/ nobody else"	(clearly) emphasises uniqueness
	repetition of "we have no"	(clearly) emphasises uniqueness

One mark for feature, one for evaluative comment

14. Unusual/unconventional/strange/ironic/quaint/ peculiar

15. *Any one example and explanation from:*

"mass ranks"	recapitulates idea of large numbers
"Terracotta Army"	returns to an expression used in opening paragraph
"(breathtaking) megalomania"	recapitulates ideas/word used earlier
"wonders of the world"	recapitulates idea of magnificence
"(The telling of that story is long) overdue"	recapitulates idea of undeserved anonymity

ENGLISH INTERMEDIATE 2 CRITICAL ESSAY 2010

Please see Critical Essay Marking Principles on pages 64–65.

ENGLISH INTERMEDIATE 2
CLOSE READING
2011

1. (a) Any of "vandals", "(what) Genghis Khan (did to his neighbours)", "destroying", "pillaging", "savaging"

(b) Idea of alliteration
or similarity / balance of construction
e.g. both three-word phrases, both participial phrases, both containing "our"
or
identification of (humorous effect of) hyperbole

2.

textese	suffix "–ese" is pejorative
slanguage	(portmanteau) inclusion of "slang" is denigratory
virus	(metaphor) suggests destructiveness / disease / being harmful or unwanted
bleak	suggests (e.g.) poverty of language
bald	suggests (e.g.) plainness of language
sad	suggests regret about development or (more colloquial sense of) inadequacy
drab	suggests (e.g.) dreariness / monotony of language
shrinktalk	suggests impoverishment or (Orwellian) connotation of "-talk" suffix
masks	suggests (unwelcome) concealment of (unpalatable) truth

3. They are examples of "(new) technology" / mediums of communication which was/were originally unwanted / (needlessly) frightened people / proved to be non-harmful / beneficial

answers also acceptable which refer to the historical progression showing it is a repeated phenomenon

4. (a) They were varied / differing / contrasting / controversial / intense

(b) *Word choice:*
   • Comment may be on
   • the varied / contradictory nature of words used:
     NB comment, not mere identification (may be exemplified, e.g. opposing nature of "antagonism" and "enthusiasm")
   • **or** "such" suggesting intensity of reactions
   • **or** "phenomenon" suggests (e.g.) social concern
   • **or** "all at once" suggests disturbing / contradictory nature of reactions

   Structure:
   • comment will be on **list** suggesting multiplicity or **question** being rhetorical or inviting agreement – must be more than mere identification of feature

5. *Any two from:*

Contradiction of "its distinctiveness is not a new phenomenon"	eg (the language) being different is new-fangled/modern/recent
Contradiction of "its use [is] restricted to the young"	eg only children/juveniles/teenagers use it
Contradiction of "it helps rather than hinders literacy"	eg it impedes/restricts/obstructs linguistic/verbal competence
Contradiction of "its long-term impact is negligible"	eg it will have a significant effect
Contradiction of "it is not a disaster"	eg it is a tragedy

6. Just as "hysteria" suggests panic / extremity / irrationality
So the reaction to (innovative) text message language has been excessive / needless / illogical

7. He uses "stories", "reports", "no one was ever able to track down the entire essay"
and "(probably a) hoax", "quoted incessantly"
or
quotation of one of these and comment on its contribution to the sense of untruth and/or credulousness
or
he tells the (apocryphal) essay story / gives an example
to show what people were willing to believe

8. Both are acronyms / formed from initial letters / abbreviations.

9. Glosses of **two** of "English has had abbreviated words ever since it began to be written down" – eg this is not new/has a long history
And "attracted criticism" or "complained" – eg have always had a hostile reception/met with disapproval
And "have effectively become new words" – eg have been accepted into the language in their own right

10. They are proof of his point
about literary respectability/long history of deviant forms
or
An assertion that the candidate has no/little idea who these people are
And so this does not help his argument/make anything clear

11. The letters which are used most often (gloss of "frequently occurring")
are not the most easily/most quickly written (gloss of "access" or "input")

12. "Abbreviations" or "(intuitive) response" introduces/points **forward** (to the contractions/reactions covered in the remainder of the paragraph); "technological problem" refers **back** (to the difficulties of entering letters mentioned in the previous paragraph)

13. It signals or introduces a contrast / contributes to a link
Between the practical/technical reasons behind aspects of text language (he has been examining)
And the other (psychological) ones (he goes on to explore)

14. Doubt/disagreement/cynicism/contention/irony/sarcasm

15. Knowledge about/sensitivity to language

16. Answers must relate some aspect of this paragraph to another feature or idea mentioned or used earlier in the passage

Aspect from last paragraph	Reference to elsewhere
Idea of dislike of or bemusement at texting	repeats idea of aversion mentioned in eg opening paragraphs.
Idea of creativity or adaptability	repeats idea of flexibility of language, in eg its not being a new phenomenon.
"There is no disaster pending"	echoes reassurances given elsewhere, eg in "it is not a disaster".
"We will not see a new generation of adults growing up unable to write proper English"/"The language as a whole will not decline"	repeats idea of children's linguistic awareness.
"texting…is language in evolution"	repeats idea of development mentioned elsewhere, eg in adoption of new abbreviated forms.
Upbeat, positive tone of last paragraph	echoes optimistic, affirmative tone throughout the passage (may be exemplified).

ENGLISH INTERMEDIATE 2 CLOSE READING 2012

1. odd/strange/curious/eccentric – ie not comical/amusing

2. Any one of "beloved", "bizarre", "twists" or "(poor) dears" suggests (e.g.) amusement/condescension/wonderment/lack of sympathy/mockery
   or
   any other acceptable comment **on the chosen example**

3. "(these multifarious) superstitions" or "(not only about) humanity" looks back to the ideas of the first two paragraphs "of deeper importance" anticipates more serious ideas which follow
   or
   "other species" anticipates following ideas (about pigeons)
   or
   "not only (about humanity)" signals a diversion
   or
   the question the sentence asks is then answered

4. Glosses of "widely regarded" (e.g. seen by many people/well-known/respected) or "father (of modern psychology)" (e.g. an innovative/authoritative figure)
   or
   Skinner used pigeons in his experiments

5. It (clearly) conveys the innovative nature of the experiment/he was doing something new
   or
   the expression may be perceived as a cliché

6. Both the pigeons and the tennis player (wrongly) thought their actions were linked to the consequences

7. It adds/contributes to the humour/sceptical tone of the passage

8. (To show that) intelligent people can be superstitious too/ superstition is not just the preserve of "the silly and gullible"

9. There is the (literal) sense of being malodorous and the (figurative) sense of being annoying
   or
   The pun/double meaning/play on words of (literal and figurative) senses of being malodorous and being annoying

10. (a) They give an example/provide an illustration which addresses the reason(s) for superstition/continues the idea of "deep evolutionary history"

    (b) This is a modern/idealistic notion
    In a very old/more brutal context
    Condensed answer explaining incongruity/anachronism

11. Gloss of "providing a cocoon of safety in a turbulent and dangerous world": e.g. they insulate/shield/shelter/protect in unstable/risky/perilous/unsettled circumstances
    or
    gloss of "The caveman's behaviour now looks not only sensible but life-saving" e.g. being superstitious can make you cautious and (therefore) more likely to survive

12. It introduces an expansion or explanation (of what the "proviso" is).

13. (a) People (still) indulge in superstition (in various situations)
    But it has little influence/(beneficial) effect/is harmless

    (b) Idea of similarity of construction/repetition/triplet of "some… but"
    or
    comparability of relationship indicated/implied by use of semi-colons (N.B. not identification of semi-colon alone)

14.

It is appropriate because	Just as a spectrum contains a whole range/variety/scale (of colours)	so there is a (wide) range of superstitions/ (illogical) behaviours/ perceptions/beliefs
It is inappropriate because	the (bright) colour imagery implied	is not apt or fitting or helpful to describe/illustrate the (melancholy) subject

15. It illustrates his point about the range of "irrationality" by providing an extreme example of superstition

or

It illustrates his point that superstition taken to excess/ dogmatically insisted upon has an unhelpful/deleterious effect/outcome

or

He is using reference to a team game to show the influence of superstition on others

or

He is using someone famous to help the reader connect

16. The reference to the elements of help and hindrance (neatly) recaps the idea of ambivalence explored elsewhere in the passage

or

"ritual" (tellingly) repeats a (significant) word used earlier/repeated (three times) earlier in the passage

or

(metaphor) "kick (the ritual into touch)" (neatly) reprises references to football/sport used earlier

or

"a rabbit's foot" is (clearly) associated with superstition which is the article's topic

or

"With a rabbit's foot, obviously" (adroitly) reprises the cynical/sceptical/humorous tone seen elsewhere

ENGLISH INTERMEDIATE 2
CRITICAL ESSAY
2008 TO 2012 EXAMS

Marking Principles for the Critical Essay are as follows:

- The essay should first be read to establish whether the essay achieves success in **all** the Performance Criteria for Grade C, including relevance and the standards for technical accuracy outlined in Note 1 below.
- If minimum standards are not achieved in any **one** or more of the Performance Criteria, the maximum mark which can be awarded is 11.
- If minimum standards have been achieved, then the supplementary marking grids will allow you to place the work on a scale of marks out of 25.
- The Category awarded and the mark should be placed at the end of the essay.

Notes:

1. "Sufficiently accurate" can best be defined in terms of a definition of "consistently accurate".
   - *Consistently accurate*
     A few errors may be present, but these will not be significant in any way. The candidate may use some complex vocabulary and sentence structures. Where appropriate, sentences will show accurate handling of clauses. Linking between sentences will be clear. Paragraphing will reflect a developing line of thought.

   - *Sufficiently accurate*
     As above but with an allowance made for speed and the lack of opportunity to redraft.

2. Using the Category descriptions

   - Categories are not grades. Although derived from performance criteria at C and the indicators of excellence for Grade A, the four categories are designed primarily to assist with placing each candidate response at an appropriate point on a continuum of achievement. Assumptions about final grades or association of final grades with particular categories should not be allowed to influence objective assessment.

   - Once an essay has been deemed to pass the basic criteria, it does not have to meet all the suggestions for Category II (for example) to fall into that Category. More typically there will be a spectrum of strengths and weaknesses which span categories.

GRADE C
Performance Criteria

(a) *Understanding*
   As appropriate to task, the response demonstrates understanding of key elements, central concerns and significant details of the text(s).

(b) *Analysis*
   The response explains in some detail ways in which aspects of structure/style/language contribute to meaning/effect/impact.

(c) *Evaluation*
   The response reveals engagement with the text(s) or aspects of the text(s) and stated or implied evaluation of effectiveness, substantiated by some relevant evidence from the text(s).

(d) *Expression*
   Structure, style and language, including use of some appropriate critical terminology, are deployed to communicate meaning clearly and develop a line of thought which is generally relevant to purpose; spelling, grammar and punctuation are sufficiently accurate.

It should be noted that the term "text" encompasses printed, audio or film/video text(s) which may be literary (fiction or non-fiction) or may relate to aspects of media or language.

Language Questions 13 - 15

- The "text" which should be dealt with in a language question is the research which the pupil has done. Examples taken from their research must be there for you to see.
- However, to demonstrate understanding and analysis related to these examples there has to be some ability to generalise from the particular, to classify and comment on what has been discovered. It is not enough merely to produce a list of words in, say, Dundonian with their standard English equivalents. This is merely description and without any further development does not demonstrate understanding of any principle underlying the choice of words.
- The list of features at the head of the section is supportive. A marker would reasonably expect that some such features would be mentioned in the course of the candidate's answer.

Intermediate 2 Critical Essay Supplementary Advice

This advice, which is supplementary to the published Performance Criteria, is designed to assist with the placing of scripts within the full range of marks. However, the Performance Criteria as published give the primary definitions.

The mark range for each Category is identified.

IV 8–11	III 12–15	II 16–19	I 20–25
• An essay which falls into this category may do so for a variety of reasons.	**Understanding** • Knowledge of the text(s), and a basic understanding of the **main** concerns will be used .... to provide an answer which is **generally relevant** to the task.	**Understanding** • Knowledge and understanding of the **central** concerns of the text(s) will be used .... to provide an answer which is **mainly relevant** to the task.	**Understanding** • **Secure** knowledge **and some insight** into the central concerns of the text(s) will be demonstrated at this level .... and there will be a line of thought which is **consistently relevant** to the task.
It could be • that it fails to achieve sufficient technical accuracy • or that any knowledge and understanding of the material is not deployed as a response relevant to the task • or that analysis and evaluation attempted are unconvincing • or that the answer is simply too thin.	• Some reference to the text(s) will be made to **support** the candidate's argument.	• Reference to the text(s) will be used as evidence to **promote** the candidate's argument.	• Reference to the text(s) will be used **appropriately** as evidence which helps to **develop** the argument **fully**.
	Analysis • There will be an **explanation** of the contribution of literary/linguistic techniques to the impact of the text(s).	**Analysis** • There will be an **explanation of the effectiveness** of the contribution of literary/linguistic techniques to the impact of the text(s).	**Analysis** • There will be **some insight** shown into the **effectiveness** of the contribution of literary/linguistic techniques to the impact of the text(s).
	Evaluation • There will be **some engagement** with the text(s) which will state or imply an evaluation of its effectiveness.	**Evaluation** • There will be **engagement** with the text(s) which leads to a **generally valid** evaluative stance with respect to the text(s).	**Evaluation** • There will be a **clear engagement** with the text(s) which leads to a **valid** evaluative stance with respect to the material.
	Expression • Language will communicate the argument clearly, and there will be appropriate critical terminology deployed. Spelling, grammar and punctuation will be sufficiently accurate.	**Expression** • Language will communicate the argument **clearly**, and there will be appropriate critical terminology deployed **to aid the argument**. Spelling, grammar and punctuation will be sufficiently accurate.	**Expression** • The language will communicate **effectively** making appropriate use of critical terminology **to further the argument**. Spelling, grammar and punctuation will be sufficiently accurate.

Hey! I've done it

iBrightRED
PUBLISHING

© 2012 SQA/Bright Red Publishing Ltd, All Rights Reserved
Published by Bright Red Publishing Ltd, 6 Stafford Street, Edinburgh, EH3 7AU
Tel: 0131 220 5804, Fax: 0131 220 6710, enquiries: sales@brightredpublishing.co.uk,
www.brightredpublishing.co.uk

Official SQA answers to 978-1-84948-270-7
2008-2012